Inquiries regarding permission for use of the material contained in this book should be addressed to:

CornerStone Leadership Institute
P.O. Box 764087
Dallas, TX 75376
888.789.LEAD

Printed in China
ISBN: 978-0-9821246-0-4

Library of Congress Control Number: 2012939553

Manufactured in China through InterPress Ltd.
September 2012 - Job# 121023

Credits
Editor   Julie Cope, Franklin, TN
Copy editor   Kathleen Green, Positively Proofed, Plano, TX
                                                    info@positivelyproofed.com
Design, art direction, and production   Melissa Monogue, Back Porch Creative, Plano, TX
                                                    info@backporchcreative.com

Monday Morning Leadership

FOR KIDS

with Baxter & Paw Paw

Evelyn Addis & David Cottrell

Illustrated by Matt Loughmiller

CornerStone
Leadership Institute

*This book is dedicated to all the teachers,
parents, grandparents, and friends
who share their wisdom and time
to develop positive character traits in kids.*

A Note from the Author

As a teacher of young children for over thirty-five years, I am always looking for new and exciting ways to engage my students. I want to teach them not just about reading, math, and science, but also about right and wrong, making good choices, and being responsible.

When I read David Cottrell's book *Monday Morning Leadership*, I was struck by how simple yet profound his messages of the importance of character and how to develop it were. I thought the story, which focused on a relationship between a young man and his older mentor, would adapt well for my students. I contacted David, and we began a collaboration that resulted in the book you are now holding in your hands.

My students helped me along the way as I wrote and refined the story, and they loved it. It is my hope that the story of Baxter and Paw Paw and the lessons taught and learned will be a great place for you to begin your own conversations with the young people in your life.

Evelyn Addis

It's Monday morning. I wake up, look at the clock, and jump out of bed. My Paw Paw is going to be here soon!

Paw Paw and I get to spend time together every Monday morning.

Paw Paw is so smart, and that's why I listen very carefully to everything he tells me.

Oh, there's my Paw Paw's truck. I have to hurry!

I open the front door and give Paw Paw a big hug.

"Baxter, we're going on a special trip today," announces Paw Paw. "I am going to teach you how to drive."

"But, Paw Paw, I'm too little to drive."

Paw Paw smiles and says, "Yes, you *are* too little to drive a car, but you are *not* too little to be a good driver of your character."

"What is character, Paw Paw?"

"Baxter, your character is who you are on the inside."

"Paw Paw, how can I be a great driver of my character?"

"What a great question, Baxter! I think you will learn the answer on our trip today."

I climb up into Paw Paw's big red truck and fasten my seatbelt. Paw Paw starts the engine, and we are on our way.

I like that Paw Paw's big truck lets me sit way up high. I can see everything as we ride down the road.

"Baxter, look at all the cars. Every car has only one driver. To drive your character, you must accept responsibility for your actions. Every decision includes choices. You can choose to do the *right* thing or the *wrong* thing."

"So that means I need to make good choices!"

"That's it exactly, Baxter. Your choices always affect you, and others too. If one driver makes a bad choice, it will affect the drivers of all the other cars. Think very carefully before you act when you have a decision to make."

Paw Paw reaches over and rubs me on the head. "Baxter, you and I are in for a great day."

Paw Paw's truck turns down Main Street. Red lights are flashing from a police car. Two cars have collided.

"What happened, Paw Paw?" I ask.

"It looks like one of the drivers didn't stop at the stop sign," Paw Paw answers.

That makes me think about what Paw Paw just taught me. Every decision affects more than one person.

Paw Paw says, "Someone did not keep their eyes on the main thing."

"What was the main thing, Paw Paw?"

15

"Well, in this case, Baxter, the main thing was for the driver to obey the law and stop at the stop sign. You should always figure out what is the most important thing to do in a situation. What do you think that would be when you are at home?"

"Hmmm . . . I think I should do what my parents ask me to do."

"That's right, Baxter! You should obey the people who are responsible for you because they always want what is best for you."

I think about this for a minute. "So, if my mom asks me to clean up my room, I should do a really good job, and pick up all my toys and make my bed and put away my dirty clothes."

"Good job! And what about at school?" Paw Paw asks me.

"I should listen, follow directions, and complete all of my work. And I shouldn't whine or complain."

"Baxter, those are great examples of some of the main things at home and at school. You are understanding what character means!"

Paw Paw gives me a high five!

Paw Paw's big truck chugs up Steep Hill Road. We're almost close enough for me to touch the sky.

"Baxter, did you know that there are millions and millions of stars in the sky? At night, you can see the sky full of them! Some of them are so far away we can barely see them, and some are so close that they are very bright. What kind of star would you like to be?"

"I don't know, Paw Paw. Let's close our eyes and pretend it's nighttime. What do you see?"

"Baxter, right in the middle of the sky, I see a big shining star!"

"That star is me, Paw Paw! That's the star I want to be!"

"How do you think you can shine brightly, Baxter?"

"I guess I can shine by always doing my best at home, at school . . . well, really, in whatever I'm doing. And you know what, Paw Paw? I think a shining star would encourage others to shine as brightly as they can too."

Paw Paw claps and claps! "Way to go, Baxter!"

Paw Paw's big truck hums along as we sing our favorite song. Suddenly Paw Paw stops the truck.

"Why are we stopping here?" I ask.

"Do you see that sign? It says DO NOT ENTER! There must be some kind of danger ahead."

"Can't we just drive around that sign? No one will see us."

"Yes, I suppose we could do that, but would that be a good choice? Oh, Baxter, you should always do the right thing, even when no one is watching."

"But, Paw Paw, sometimes that's hard to do."

"Yes, I know. But it's important to do the right thing. You will feel good, and people will know they can count on you to make good choices."

Paw Paw turns the big truck around. We smile because we know we did the right thing.

I keep thinking, *Always, always, always do the right thing, even when no one is watching.*

Paw Paw's truck rumbles along the road until we come to a soccer field.

I can see a red team and a blue team playing. Paw Paw parks the truck so that we can watch the soccer game.

"Baxter, see how these teams work together. Teammates encourage each other. Do you hear them telling each other, 'Good job'? You need to be around people who encourage you too. Choose your friends very carefully."

30

"Paw Paw, how do you choose your friends?"

"Baxter, friendships are sort of like you are all on the same team. You want to have friends who help you be a better person. We must be kind and show respect to everyone, but who you hang out with is very important! And to have good friends, you must be a good friend."

"I get it, Paw Paw. I need to choose friends who also want to do the right thing."

"Baxter, you are so smart!"

"Are you hungry, Baxter? Let's sit on the back of the truck and eat our lunch."

Paw Paw always packs a yummy lunch for us and I'm getting pretty hungry, so I like this idea.

Paw Paw parks the truck so that we can see the enormous clock on top of the bank building.

"Baxter, see that big clock up there. We all have the same amount of time each day. How we use our time is very important."

I take a bite of my sandwich and watch the hands of that giant clock. Wow, they never stop moving! I think, *Time doesn't stop for anyone!*

"Paw Paw, I think I understand. To be a great driver of my character, I need to be smart with how I use my time."

"It's a great lesson to learn now, Baxter, because every second that goes by is gone forever. Oh, and by the way, it's TIME to go."

Paw Paw winks at me. We throw away our trash and climb back in the truck.

Paw Paw's big truck makes the turn to start home. I ask if we can drive by the big construction site near my house. I want to watch those giant trucks.

Paw Paw pulls the truck close so we have a great view. We see dump trucks being filled by backhoes and dump trucks emptying their loads.

"Baxter, people are kind of like those trucks. We all have a bucket like the dump truck, and we all have a dipper like the backhoe."

"Paw Paw, I don't have a bucket or a dipper!"

"Oh, yes, you do, Baxter. You just can't see it. We all have an invisible bucket inside of us. Other people can fill our bucket by being kind and respectful to us. But we also have a dipper that will empty someone's bucket when we are unkind or disrespectful to them. I call this our bucket of encouragement."

"So if I treat someone the way I want to be treated, I will be a bucket-filler? And if I say unkind things or do something unkind, I will be a bucket-dipper?"

"That's the way it works, Baxter. But the greatest part of being a bucket-filler is that when you fill someone else's bucket, you also fill your own bucket. Being kind and respectful to others makes you feel good inside."

"Wow, Paw Paw! Today YOU filled my bucket!"

Paw Paw laughs and says, "And YOU filled MY bucket too."

Paw Paw's big truck turns down my street, and I can see my house.

Paw Paw says we should call my home "The Learning Zone."

"Well, okay, but we just call it home."

"Baxter, you need to practice having good character all the time, and home is the best place to start."

"Paw Paw, thanks for a great day! I love our Mondays together. I promise I will practice everything you've taught me."

Paw Paw laughs a great big bear laugh. "I had a great day too, Baxter. And when you get older, I will teach you how to drive my truck."

I run and give him a great big bear hug.

"Bye, Paw Paw."

"Bye, Baxter."

"Love you!"

"Love you too!"

Teacher and Parent Curriculum Guide

Reinforce the character attributes in *Monday Morning Leadership for Kids* with a ready-to-use, downloadable, reproducible Teacher and Parent Curriculum guide. The guide includes:

- Detailed lesson plans to be used in science, math, social studies, reading, and writing

- Student "driver's license"

- Symbols for each of the eight character attributes

- Coloring puppets of Baxter and Paw Paw

All this and more for only $20.

www.CornerStoneLeadership.com   888-789-5323

Recommended Reading from CornerStone Leadership

Monday Morning Leadership: 8 Mentoring Sessions You Can't Afford to Miss

Monday Morning Leadership for Women

Listen Up, Teacher . . . YOU Are Making a Difference

Inspire! Connecting with Students to Make a Difference

www.CornerStoneLeadership.com   888-789-5323

About the Authors & Illustrator

EveLyn ADDis has been an educator of young children for 36 years. Her passion is teaching children to read while instilling in them the love of books. Evelyn is the author of *Come Walk with Me*, a teaching manual for educators of young children. She and her toy poodle, Brandy, live in Canton, Texas.

DaviD CottReLL is the author of over 25 books, including the best-selling *Monday Morning Leadership*. He is the president and CEO of CornerStone Leadership Institute. Just like Paw Paw, David loves spending time with his five grandchildren—Noah, Pearce, Asa, Hunt, and Charlotte. David and his wife, Karen, live in Horseshoe Bay, Texas.

Matt Loughmiller is an artist and art teacher. Matt has been in public education for over 20 years and has taught all grades from kindergarten through twelfth. He was attracted to education because of his love of art and the fulfillment of working with kids. Matt lives in East Texas with his wife, Diane.

The authors and illustrator can be reached at info@CornerStoneLeadership.com.